the NOURISH NOTEBOOK

90-DAY HABIT PRACTICE GUIDE

A Mind-Body Eating Experience for Freedom

written by

DIANE CUNNINGHAM ELLIS

A **BRAVE CREATIONS** BOOK

You'll never change your life until you change something you do daily. The secret of your success is found in your

Daily Routine.

JOHN C. MAXWELL

DEDICATION

I dedicate this book to my husband, Jim. I am intimately aware of his relentless nourishment of me, my dreams, and our life together. Babe, thank you for always inviting me to become my best self and encouraging my lifelong transformation.

ACKNOWLEDGEMENTS

Thank you to the women I coach, consult, mentor and teach. In every group, program, process, and retreat. The women who allow me to see into their life journey and gently guide and support. The women of the Life Change Club, Nourish, Brave Creations Inner Circle, and all of the things I have created in my 20-plus years of coaching. I cannot do this work without you.

Thank you to Callie Revell who helps me to exist in my brilliance by working with me behind the scenes on every project. I would be amiss and adrift without you, Callie! You are a delight.

God, thank you for teaching me to love myself in a new and nourishing way. I promise to keep going, just for today... One day at a time. I promise to practice being in this body and cherishing it. To nourish myself in all of the ways you designed for us!

TABLE OF CONTENTS

HELLO, FRIENDS!

Nourishment. We need it. It is a long-lost art for most of us. A glimpse into self-care and thoughts of spa treatments and other images arise.

I believe this Nourish **Notebook** is a crucial tool in our recovery from food addictions, overgiving, martyrdom, and people pleasing. I believe that it is a way to *see* what your life and food and journey reveals to you. Think of this as an archeological dig and the subject is you, your heart, your cravings, your story. That includes food, your surroundings, your rhythms, and your routines.

Believe me... I have used every type of planner and system and tracker for business, my food, and all sorts of things I have created many of my own worksheets, templates, and fill-in-the-blanks to add to my planner. I have used ring bound and spiral bound. I have used small, medium, and large sized. I use wall calendars, too. I use notebooks and post-its and all of the "things."

I believe in transformation, and I believe in nourishment. I also believe that I have changed my life, my body, my business, and my income by using very simple written tracking tools.

Thus, I finally decided to create the **Nourish Notebook** and the other companion notebook, the **Transformation Tracker**. One is more focused on life and food and body changes, and one is focused on business. Both are actually adaptable by you and will become what you need them to be for a 90-day period of time.

Why 90 days? I know that it takes longer than we want it to. I love working in 90-day increments with my coaching clients, and it gives us time to see patterns and trends and have a few meltdowns that lead to miracles.

INSTRUCTIONS FOR THE JOURNEY — LET'S DIVE IN!

Getting Started

This book is blank and set up to be used for a 90-day journey. Start today. Or wait. But I know my biggest changes started when I was forced into "rock bottom," and it wasn't pretty. You can choose to change today... You do not have to wait until Monday, the new month, the new year, or any other self-defeating concept we can come up with. There is no perfect day. I want you to wreck this notebook/journal with your writing, post-it notes, highlighting, and tabs. I want to see your journey on paper. I want you to be transformed.

Tips and Tricks

You can get this paperback book cut and spiral bound at your local office supply store for around $6. That is what I suggest. Then, it will lay flat and will be easier to write in. But hey... whatever works for you!

Writing Prompts (p. 16)

Start with the 90 Days of Nourishment.

Monthly Calendars (p. 18)

Fill in the dates. Easy enough.

Habit Trackers (p. 19)

I use these often for business habits, life habits, and home habits. You can download a PDF version on my website for FREE Here:
dianecunningham.com/nourishgift

Food Log Weekly Spread Pages (p. 24)

You can use these in two ways: to plan your food for the day or as a log of the food you have chosen to eat each day. Whatever works for you, or both. Write down your gratitude and challenges... practice awareness. There are 12 weeks of these pages.

Affirmations and Aha's Pages (p. 48)

Write down your aha's and awakenings related to you nourish journey. What we acknowledge, we can remember better. And writing it down is a key to our inner transformation. Awareness. Acceptance.

Lessons Learned Pages (p. 52)

I always ask my clients to use this question for self-coaching... "What did you learn today about yourself, other people, or the world?" It is a powerful reminder that every day is a lesson in caring for ourselves. Nourishment is a practice, not a one-hit wonder.

Gratitude Jar (p. 57)

A fun way to write down your gratitudes as you go along. Another idea is to actually create your own version of this using a mason jar at home. Why not? I had one for years that said "Surrender Jar" on it, and it was on my kitchen window sill. You can also print this out as a free gift on my website: *dianecunningham.com/nourishgift*

Food Lists Pages (p. 58)

This is a homework assignment that I give all of my clients. We write down 33 foods we like and 33 foods that we dislike or don't work for our body (allergies, sensitivities, textures). This list alone is a huge moment of clarity and brings up all sorts of things. We are so used to living on a diet and with "diet mentality" that this list frightens us. I suggest you allow yourself permission to be honest here. I have learned over my last few years that I loved certain foods that I thought I "hated." And I have learned many foods that I enjoy eating in the moment but cause me body pain or inflammation/digestion problems later.

Meal Ideas Pages (p. 60)

Now we take our list of 33 foods we like and we write down 2 or 3 breakfasts that we enjoy that are in our food plan. What is a FOOD PLAN? I will cover that next. We write down 2-3 lunches that we actually want to eat. We might write down 4-5 dinners that we enjoy. We tend to eat the same things over and over again. I have read that the normal woman makes 250 food decisions a day... this helps take some of the confusion away. We have our foods and we plan our week. We plan and know some places we can eat out and still remain on track with our goals.

Food Plan Page (p. 64)

A food plan is the type of eating you want to do. We have often called this a "diet." When I learned to call it a food plan and a lifestyle, that is when I was able to release extra pounds that I did not need to hold onto anymore.

I have had a variety of food plans over the past few years of this recent transformation. What you want to do is learn what works for your body. That might be keto, or paleo, or plant based. It might include foods I don't eat. Your food plan is different in the heat of the summer than it might be in January. Our bodies are different. The way we live and our location affects our food plan. If you are in a tropical climate, you might eat differently than a bitter cold location.

You can create a "temporary food plan" to get started. My first food plan was just 3 meals and 2 optional snacks. That gave me some boundaries and helped me learn. Then, I removed some foods and felt better. My food plan changed. Like I said, it has adapted and morphed many times over the past 2-plus years. Your food plan will become a part of you, but you are not married to it. My body has changed, too, as I found out I needed medication for my thyroid. So, my food plan adapts with me as I learn, grow, and my body changes. That is part of learning how to nourish myself.

Hunger Scale (p. 65)

This scale will help you to see and learn from your eating. I often still am not sure of my hunger. When we have dieted for decades, we stop listening. We follow the system, the rules, the process. This program is about unlearning all of the guru-given perfection... This nourish program is about learning *you*.

Learning your hunger, learning your fullness, learning what enough is. Learning your body, learning your cravings. Learning to eat.

Habit Creation Pages (p. 66)

I included 3 Habit Creation Plan pages. These help us see beneath the surface. Why? Why does this nourishment plan matter? Why do you want to release the weight? Why do you want to feel better? Why will this be worth it? Habit change is hard. We just keep doing what we say we don't want to do!

I do not understand what I do. For what I want to do I do not do, but what I hate to do. —Romans 7:15 NIV

Awareness of your habit allows you the opportunity to change it. The same way we let go of any addictive behavior... one day at a time. It is how I have chosen sobriety since June of 2013. I choose again today. One day at a time.

Nourish Daily Practice Pages (p. 72)

90 pages for your daily writing. Practicing. Morning and evening. Awareness and focus. Gratitude and commitments. Willingness to be willing.

In the same way, husbands ought to love their wives as their own bodies. He who loves his wife loves himself. Indeed, no one ever hated his own body, but he nourishes and cherishes it, just as Christ does the church. For we are members of His body. —Ephesians 5:29

Are you ready to be practice nourishing yourself?

Are you ready to be transformed by writing a few things down?

By noticing, by paying attention.

We often just need to pray for the willingness to be willing and then keep showing up.

You can do this! Here's to your transformation and nourishment success!

LOVE,

Diane Cunningham Ellis

90 DAYS OF NOURISHMENT

My **Nourishment Plan** for the next 90 Days includes the desire to reach certain goals or change these behaviors/habits:

1.

2.

3.

I want to reach these milestones (or goals) so that...

To me, nourishment includes...

What mindsets do you need to let go of? Excuses?

1.

2.

3.

4.

5.

How can you let it be easy? Or stop overthinking this?

I commit to this because...

MY NOURISHMENT PLAN

YEAR:

MONTH:

HABIT TRACKER

MONTH:

HABIT	DATE	1	2	3	4	5	6	7	8	9	10	11	12	13	14	15	16	17	18	19	20	21	22	23	24	25	26	27	28	29	30	31

YEAR:

MONTH:

HABIT TRACKER

MONTH:

HABIT	DATE	1	2	3	4	5	6	7	8	9	10	11	12	13	14	15	16	17	18	19	20	21	22	23	24	25	26	27	28	29	30	31

YEAR:

MONTH:

HABIT TRACKER

MONTH:

HABIT \ DATE	1	2	3	4	5	6	7	8	9	10	11	12	13	14	15	16	17	18	19	20	21	22	23	24	25	26	27	28	29	30	31

FOOD LOG/PLAN FOR THE WEEK OF:

	MONDAY	TUESDAY	WEDNESDAY
BREAKFAST			
SNACK			
LUNCH			
SNACK			
DINNER			
SNACK			
OTHER (GUM, CANDY, ALCOHOL)			
PHYSICAL ACTIVITY			
TOTAL WATER			
BIGGEST CHALLENGE			
GRATITUDE			

THURSDAY	FRIDAY	SATURDAY	SUNDAY

FOOD LOG/PLAN FOR THE WEEK OF:

	MONDAY	TUESDAY	WEDNESDAY
BREAKFAST			
SNACK			
LUNCH			
SNACK			
DINNER			
SNACK			
OTHER (GUM, CANDY, ALCOHOL)			
PHYSICAL ACTIVITY			
TOTAL WATER			
BIGGEST CHALLENGE			
GRATITUDE			

THURSDAY	FRIDAY	SATURDAY	SUNDAY

FOOD LOG/PLAN FOR THE WEEK OF:

	MONDAY	TUESDAY	WEDNESDAY
BREAKFAST			
SNACK			
LUNCH			
SNACK			
DINNER			
SNACK			
OTHER (GUM, CANDY, ALCOHOL)			
PHYSICAL ACTIVITY			
TOTAL WATER			
BIGGEST CHALLENGE			
GRATITUDE			

THURSDAY	FRIDAY	SATURDAY	SUNDAY

FOOD LOG/PLAN FOR THE WEEK OF:

	MONDAY	TUESDAY	WEDNESDAY
BREAKFAST			
SNACK			
LUNCH			
SNACK			
DINNER			
SNACK			
OTHER (GUM, CANDY, ALCOHOL)			
PHYSICAL ACTIVITY			
TOTAL WATER			
BIGGEST CHALLENGE			
GRATITUDE			

THURSDAY	FRIDAY	SATURDAY	SUNDAY

FOOD LOG/PLAN FOR THE WEEK OF:

	MONDAY	TUESDAY	WEDNESDAY
BREAKFAST			
SNACK			
LUNCH			
SNACK			
DINNER			
SNACK			
OTHER (GUM, CANDY, ALCOHOL)			
PHYSICAL ACTIVITY			
TOTAL WATER			
BIGGEST CHALLENGE			
GRATITUDE			

THURSDAY	FRIDAY	SATURDAY	SUNDAY

FOOD LOG/PLAN FOR THE WEEK OF:

	MONDAY	TUESDAY	WEDNESDAY
BREAKFAST			
SNACK			
LUNCH			
SNACK			
DINNER			
SNACK			
OTHER (GUM, CANDY, ALCOHOL)			
PHYSICAL ACTIVITY			
TOTAL WATER			
BIGGEST CHALLENGE			
GRATITUDE			

FOOD LOG & PLAN FOR THE WEEK

THURSDAY	FRIDAY	SATURDAY	SUNDAY

FOOD LOG/PLAN FOR THE WEEK OF:

	MONDAY	TUESDAY	WEDNESDAY
BREAKFAST			
SNACK			
LUNCH			
SNACK			
DINNER			
SNACK			
OTHER (GUM, CANDY, ALCOHOL)			
PHYSICAL ACTIVITY			
TOTAL WATER			
BIGGEST CHALLENGE			
GRATITUDE			

FOOD LOG/PLAN FOR THE WEEK OF:

THURSDAY	FRIDAY	SATURDAY	SUNDAY

FOOD LOG/PLAN FOR THE WEEK OF:

	MONDAY	TUESDAY	WEDNESDAY
BREAKFAST			
SNACK			
LUNCH			
SNACK			
DINNER			
SNACK			
OTHER (GUM, CANDY, ALCOHOL)			
PHYSICAL ACTIVITY			
TOTAL WATER			
BIGGEST CHALLENGE			
GRATITUDE			

THURSDAY	FRIDAY	SATURDAY	SUNDAY

FOOD LOG/PLAN FOR THE WEEK OF:

	MONDAY	TUESDAY	WEDNESDAY
BREAKFAST			
SNACK			
LUNCH			
SNACK			
DINNER			
SNACK			
OTHER (GUM, CANDY, ALCOHOL)			
PHYSICAL ACTIVITY			
TOTAL WATER			
BIGGEST CHALLENGE			
GRATITUDE			

FOOD PREP PLAN FOR THE WEEK OF

THURSDAY	FRIDAY	SATURDAY	SUNDAY

FOOD LOG/PLAN FOR THE WEEK OF:

	MONDAY	TUESDAY	WEDNESDAY
BREAKFAST			
SNACK			
LUNCH			
SNACK			
DINNER			
SNACK			
OTHER (GUM, CANDY, ALCOHOL)			
PHYSICAL ACTIVITY			
TOTAL WATER			
BIGGEST CHALLENGE			
GRATITUDE			

THURSDAY	FRIDAY	SATURDAY	SUNDAY

FOOD LOG/PLAN FOR THE WEEK OF:

	MONDAY	TUESDAY	WEDNESDAY
BREAKFAST			
SNACK			
LUNCH			
SNACK			
DINNER			
SNACK			
OTHER (GUM, CANDY, ALCOHOL)			
PHYSICAL ACTIVITY			
TOTAL WATER			
BIGGEST CHALLENGE			
GRATITUDE			

THURSDAY	FRIDAY	SATURDAY	SUNDAY

FOOD LOG/PLAN FOR THE WEEK OF:

	MONDAY	TUESDAY	WEDNESDAY
BREAKFAST			
SNACK			
LUNCH			
SNACK			
DINNER			
SNACK			
OTHER (GUM, CANDY, ALCOHOL)			
PHYSICAL ACTIVITY			
TOTAL WATER			
BIGGEST CHALLENGE			
GRATITUDE			

THURSDAY	FRIDAY	SATURDAY	SUNDAY

AFFIRMATIONS AND AHA'S

AFFIRMATIONS AND AHA'S

LESSONS LEARNED

LESSONS LEARNED

GRATITUDE JAR

thank you

Food List

33 FOODS I LIKE

1.	18.
2.	19.
3.	20.
4.	21.
5.	22.
6.	23.
7.	24.
8.	25.
9.	26.
10.	27.
11.	28.
12.	29.
13.	30.
14.	31.
15.	32.
16.	33.
17.	

Food List

33 FOODS I DON'T LIKE

1.

2.

3.

4.

5.

6.

7.

8.

9.

10.

11.

12.

13.

14.

15.

16.

17.

18.

19.

20.

21.

22.

23.

24.

25.

26.

27.

28.

29.

30.

31.

32.

33.

Meal Ideas

BREAKFAST

1

2

3

Meal Ideas

LUNCH

1	

2	

3	

Meal Ideas

DINNER

1

2

3

4

5

6

7

FOOD PLAN

BREAKFAST	
SNACK	
LUNCH	
SNACK	
DINNER	
SNACK	

Nourish HUNGER SCALE

Ask. Listen. Practice.

1 — **R A V E N O U S :** fatigued, light-headed, desperate
Emotional Clues: *Who cares? I want to escape. What's the point?*

2 — **Y E A R N I N G :** irritable, uncomfortable, growly
Emotional Clues: *searching, ache, emotional unfulfillment*

3 — **H U N G R Y :** ready for nourishment, "hangry-ish"
Emotional Clues: *Wow! I am actually hungry. Not bored, distracted, angry or avoiding.*

4 — **C R A V I N G :** hunger body sensations increasing
Emotional Clues: *Hmm... I am ready to eat. My body is feeling hunger.*

5 — **N E U T R A L :** not full and not hungry; middle
Emotional Clues: *I am content. Able to focus on my life, work, and purpose.*

6 — **S A T I S F I E D :** the feeling after a snack
Emotional Clues: *That was good.*

7 — **N O U R I S H E D :** the feeling of "just right" fullness
Emotional Clues: *My belly is happy. I didn't overeat out of my emotions.*

8 — **F U L L :** a tad bit too much, uncomfortable
Emotional Clues: *That was a bit too much. I am learning. Progress, not perfection.*

9 — **B U S T I N G :** stuffed, overfull
Emotional Clues: *Too much. Ouch.*

10 — **B L O A T E D :** pants are too tight, too full, disgusted
Emotional Clues: *Miserable. Why can't I stop? I need to diet.*

HABIT CREATION PLAN

New HABIT:

Why it's important to me:

My plan to form this new HABIT:

Days and times I will commit to my new HABIT:

What can get in the way of my new HABIT goals:

Strategies and reminders that work for me when I'm tempted to stop working on my new HABITS:

HABIT CREATION PLAN

New HABIT:

Why it's important to me:

My plan to form this new HABIT:

Days and times I will commit to my new HABIT:

What can get in the way of my new HABIT goals:

Strategies and reminders that work for me when I'm tempted to stop working on my new HABITS:

HABIT CREATION PLAN

New HABIT:

_____

Why it's important to me:

_____

My plan to form this new HABIT:

_____

Days and times I will commit to my new HABIT:

_____

What can get in the way of my new HABIT goals:

_____

Strategies and reminders that work for me when I'm tempted to stop working on my new HABITS:

_____

NOURISH DAILY PRACTICE LIST

DATE:

Morning Practice

My focus word for today is:

Today I want to NOURISH myself with (and by):

I am committed to my changes today because I want...

Evening Awareness and Gratitude

Things that might NOT have been nourishing recently in my choices, eating, actions or thoughts:

My new awareness today is:

For tomorrow, I want to remember:

My WHY. I commit and recommit to this SO THAT...

NOURISH DAILY PRACTICE LIST

DATE:

Morning Practice

My focus word for today is:

Today I want to NOURISH myself with (and by):

I am committed to my changes today because I want...

Evening Awareness and Gratitude

Things that might NOT have been nourishing recently in my choices, eating, actions or thoughts:

My new awareness today is:

For tomorrow, I want to remember:

My WHY. I commit and recommit to this SO THAT...

NOURISH DAILY PRACTICE LIST

DATE:

Morning Practice

My focus word for today is:

Today I want to NOURISH myself with (and by):

I am committed to my changes today because I want...

Evening Awareness and Gratitude

Things that might NOT have been nourishing recently in my choices, eating, actions or thoughts:

My new awareness today is:

For tomorrow, I want to remember:

My WHY. I commit and recommit to this SO THAT...

NOURISH DAILY PRACTICE LIST

DATE:

Morning Practice

My focus word for today is:

Today I want to NOURISH myself with (and by):

I am committed to my changes today because I want...

Evening Awareness and Gratitude

Things that might NOT have been nourishing recently in my choices, eating, actions or thoughts:

My new awareness today is:

For tomorrow, I want to remember:

My WHY. I commit and recommit to this SO THAT...

NOURISH DAILY PRACTICE LIST

DATE:

Morning Practice

My focus word for today is:

Today I want to NOURISH myself with (and by):

I am committed to my changes today because I want...

Evening Awareness and Gratitude

Things that might NOT have been nourishing recently in my choices, eating, actions or thoughts:

My new awareness today is:

For tomorrow, I want to remember:

My WHY. I commit and recommit to this SO THAT...

NOURISH DAILY PRACTICE LIST

DATE:

Morning Practice

My focus word for today is:

Today I want to NOURISH myself with (and by):

I am committed to my changes today because I want...

Evening Awareness and Gratitude

Things that might NOT have been nourishing recently in my choices, eating, actions or thoughts:

My new awareness today is:

For tomorrow, I want to remember:

My WHY. I commit and recommit to this SO THAT...

NOURISH DAILY PRACTICE LIST

DATE:

Morning Practice

My focus word for today is:

Today I want to NOURISH myself with (and by):

I am committed to my changes today because I want...

Evening Awareness and Gratitude

Things that might NOT have been nourishing recently in my choices, eating, actions or thoughts:

My new awareness today is:

For tomorrow, I want to remember:

My WHY. I commit and recommit to this SO THAT...

NOURISH DAILY PRACTICE LIST

DATE:

Morning Practice

My focus word for today is:

Today I want to NOURISH myself with (and by):

I am committed to my changes today because I want...

Evening Awareness and Gratitude

Things that might NOT have been nourishing recently in my choices, eating, actions or thoughts:

My new awareness today is:

For tomorrow, I want to remember:

My WHY. I commit and recommit to this SO THAT...

NOURISH DAILY PRACTICE LIST

DATE:

Morning Practice

My focus word for today is:

Today I want to NOURISH myself with (and by):

I am committed to my changes today because I want...

Evening Awareness and Gratitude

Things that might NOT have been nourishing recently in my choices, eating, actions or thoughts:

My new awareness today is:

For tomorrow, I want to remember:

My WHY. I commit and recommit to this SO THAT...

NOURISH DAILY PRACTICE LIST

DATE:

Morning Practice

My focus word for today is:

Today I want to NOURISH myself with (and by):

I am committed to my changes today because I want...

Evening Awareness and Gratitude

Things that might NOT have been nourishing recently in my choices, eating, actions or thoughts:

My new awareness today is:

For tomorrow, I want to remember:

My WHY. I commit and recommit to this SO THAT...

NOURISH DAILY PRACTICE LIST

DATE:

Morning Practice

My focus word for today is:

Today I want to NOURISH myself with (and by):

I am committed to my changes today because I want...

Evening Awareness and Gratitude

Things that might NOT have been nourishing recently in my choices, eating, actions or thoughts:

My new awareness today is:

For tomorrow, I want to remember:

My WHY. I commit and recommit to this SO THAT...

NOURISH DAILY PRACTICE LIST

DATE:

Morning Practice

My focus word for today is:

Today I want to NOURISH myself with (and by):

I am committed to my changes today because I want...

Evening Awareness and Gratitude

Things that might NOT have been nourishing recently in my choices, eating, actions or thoughts:

My new awareness today is:

For tomorrow, I want to remember:

My WHY. I commit and recommit to this SO THAT...

NOURISH DAILY PRACTICE LIST

DATE:

Morning Practice

My focus word for today is:

Today I want to NOURISH myself with (and by):

I am committed to my changes today because I want...

Evening Awareness and Gratitude

Things that might NOT have been nourishing recently in my choices, eating, actions or thoughts:

My new awareness today is:

For tomorrow, I want to remember:

My WHY. I commit and recommit to this SO THAT...

NOURISH DAILY PRACTICE LIST

DATE:

Morning Practice

My focus word for today is:

Today I want to NOURISH myself with (and by):

I am committed to my changes today because I want...

Evening Awareness and Gratitude

Things that might NOT have been nourishing recently in my choices, eating, actions or thoughts:

My new awareness today is:

For tomorrow, I want to remember:

My WHY. I commit and recommit to this SO THAT...

NOURISH DAILY PRACTICE LIST

DATE:

Morning Practice

My focus word for today is:

Today I want to NOURISH myself with (and by):

I am committed to my changes today because I want...

Evening Awareness and Gratitude

Things that might NOT have been nourishing recently in my choices, eating, actions or thoughts:

My new awareness today is:

For tomorrow, I want to remember:

My WHY. I commit and recommit to this SO THAT...

NOURISH DAILY PRACTICE LIST

DATE:

Morning Practice

My focus word for today is:

Today I want to NOURISH myself with (and by):

I am committed to my changes today because I want...

Evening Awareness and Gratitude

Things that might NOT have been nourishing recently in my choices, eating, actions or thoughts:

My new awareness today is:

For tomorrow, I want to remember:

My WHY. I commit and recommit to this SO THAT...

NOURISH DAILY PRACTICE LIST

DATE:

Morning Practice

My focus word for today is:

Today I want to NOURISH myself with (and by):

I am committed to my changes today because I want…

Evening Awareness and Gratitude

Things that might NOT have been nourishing recently in my choices, eating, actions or thoughts:

My new awareness today is:

For tomorrow, I want to remember:

My WHY. I commit and recommit to this SO THAT…

NOURISH DAILY PRACTICE LIST

DATE:

Morning Practice

My focus word for today is:

Today I want to NOURISH myself with (and by):

I am committed to my changes today because I want...

Evening Awareness and Gratitude

Things that might NOT have been nourishing recently in my choices, eating, actions or thoughts:

My new awareness today is:

For tomorrow, I want to remember:

My WHY. I commit and recommit to this SO THAT...

NOURISH DAILY PRACTICE LIST

DATE:

Morning Practice

My focus word for today is:

Today I want to NOURISH myself with (and by):

I am committed to my changes today because I want...

Evening Awareness and Gratitude

Things that might NOT have been nourishing recently in my choices, eating, actions or thoughts:

My new awareness today is:

For tomorrow, I want to remember:

My WHY. I commit and recommit to this SO THAT...

NOURISH DAILY PRACTICE LIST

DATE:

Morning Practice

My focus word for today is:

Today I want to NOURISH myself with (and by):

I am committed to my changes today because I want...

Evening Awareness and Gratitude

Things that might NOT have been nourishing recently in my choices, eating, actions or thoughts:

My new awareness today is:

For tomorrow, I want to remember:

My WHY. I commit and recommit to this SO THAT...

NOURISH DAILY PRACTICE LIST

DATE:

Morning Practice

My focus word for today is:

Today I want to NOURISH myself with (and by):

I am committed to my changes today because I want...

Evening Awareness and Gratitude

Things that might NOT have been nourishing recently in my choices, eating, actions or thoughts:

My new awareness today is:

For tomorrow, I want to remember:

My WHY. I commit and recommit to this SO THAT...

NOURISH DAILY PRACTICE LIST

DATE:

Morning Practice

My focus word for today is:

Today I want to NOURISH myself with (and by):

I am committed to my changes today because I want...

Evening Awareness and Gratitude

Things that might NOT have been nourishing recently in my choices, eating, actions or thoughts:

My new awareness today is:

For tomorrow, I want to remember:

My WHY. I commit and recommit to this SO THAT...

NOURISH DAILY PRACTICE LIST

DATE:

Morning Practice

My focus word for today is:

Today I want to NOURISH myself with (and by):

I am committed to my changes today because I want...

Evening Awareness and Gratitude

Things that might NOT have been nourishing recently in my choices, eating, actions or thoughts:

My new awareness today is:

For tomorrow, I want to remember:

My WHY. I commit and recommit to this SO THAT...

NOURISH DAILY PRACTICE LIST

DATE:

Morning Practice

My focus word for today is:

Today I want to NOURISH myself with (and by):

I am committed to my changes today because I want...

Evening Awareness and Gratitude

Things that might NOT have been nourishing recently in my choices, eating, actions or thoughts:

My new awareness today is:

For tomorrow, I want to remember:

My WHY. I commit and recommit to this SO THAT...

NOURISH DAILY PRACTICE LIST

DATE:

Morning Practice

My focus word for today is:

Today I want to NOURISH myself with (and by):

I am committed to my changes today because I want...

Evening Awareness and Gratitude

Things that might NOT have been nourishing recently in my choices, eating, actions or thoughts:

My new awareness today is:

For tomorrow, I want to remember:

My WHY. I commit and recommit to this SO THAT...

NOURISH DAILY PRACTICE LIST

DATE:

Morning Practice

My focus word for today is:

Today I want to NOURISH myself with (and by):

I am committed to my changes today because I want...

Evening Awareness and Gratitude

Things that might NOT have been nourishing recently in my choices, eating, actions or thoughts:

My new awareness today is:

For tomorrow, I want to remember:

My WHY. I commit and recommit to this SO THAT...

NOURISH DAILY PRACTICE LIST

DATE:

Morning Practice

My focus word for today is:

Today I want to NOURISH myself with (and by):

I am committed to my changes today because I want...

Evening Awareness and Gratitude

Things that might NOT have been nourishing recently in my choices, eating, actions or thoughts:

My new awareness today is:

For tomorrow, I want to remember:

My WHY. I commit and recommit to this SO THAT...

NOURISH DAILY PRACTICE LIST

DATE:

Morning Practice

My focus word for today is:

Today I want to NOURISH myself with (and by):

I am committed to my changes today because I want...

Evening Awareness and Gratitude

Things that might NOT have been nourishing recently in my choices, eating, actions or thoughts:

My new awareness today is:

For tomorrow, I want to remember:

My WHY. I commit and recommit to this SO THAT...

NOURISH DAILY PRACTICE LIST

DATE:

Morning Practice

My focus word for today is:

Today I want to NOURISH myself with (and by):

I am committed to my changes today because I want...

Evening Awareness and Gratitude

Things that might NOT have been nourishing recently in my choices, eating, actions or thoughts:

My new awareness today is:

For tomorrow, I want to remember:

My WHY. I commit and recommit to this SO THAT...

NOURISH DAILY PRACTICE LIST

DATE:

Morning Practice

My focus word for today is:

Today I want to NOURISH myself with (and by):

I am committed to my changes today because I want...

Evening Awareness and Gratitude

Things that might NOT have been nourishing recently in my choices, eating, actions or thoughts:

My new awareness today is:

For tomorrow, I want to remember:

My WHY. I commit and recommit to this SO THAT...

NOURISH DAILY PRACTICE LIST

DATE:

Morning Practice

My focus word for today is:

Today I want to NOURISH myself with (and by):

I am committed to my changes today because I want...

Evening Awareness and Gratitude

Things that might NOT have been nourishing recently in my choices, eating, actions or thoughts:

My new awareness today is:

For tomorrow, I want to remember:

My WHY. I commit and recommit to this SO THAT...

NOURISH DAILY PRACTICE LIST

DATE:

Morning Practice

My focus word for today is:

Today I want to NOURISH myself with (and by):

I am committed to my changes today because I want...

Evening Awareness and Gratitude

Things that might NOT have been nourishing recently in my choices, eating, actions or thoughts:

My new awareness today is:

For tomorrow, I want to remember:

My WHY. I commit and recommit to this SO THAT...

NOURISH DAILY PRACTICE LIST

DATE:

Morning Practice

My focus word for today is:

Today I want to NOURISH myself with (and by):

I am committed to my changes today because I want...

Evening Awareness and Gratitude

Things that might NOT have been nourishing recently in my choices, eating, actions or thoughts:

My new awareness today is:

For tomorrow, I want to remember:

My WHY. I commit and recommit to this SO THAT...

NOURISH DAILY PRACTICE LIST

DATE:

Morning Practice

My focus word for today is:

Today I want to NOURISH myself with (and by):

I am committed to my changes today because I want...

Evening Awareness and Gratitude

Things that might NOT have been nourishing recently in my choices, eating, actions or thoughts:

My new awareness today is:

For tomorrow, I want to remember:

My WHY. I commit and recommit to this SO THAT...

NOURISH DAILY PRACTICE LIST

DATE:

Morning Practice

My focus word for today is:

Today I want to NOURISH myself with (and by):

I am committed to my changes today because I want...

Evening Awareness and Gratitude

Things that might NOT have been nourishing recently in my choices, eating, actions or thoughts:

My new awareness today is:

For tomorrow, I want to remember:

My WHY. I commit and recommit to this SO THAT...

NOURISH DAILY PRACTICE LIST

DATE:

Morning Practice

My focus word for today is:

Today I want to NOURISH myself with (and by):

I am committed to my changes today because I want...

Evening Awareness and Gratitude

Things that might NOT have been nourishing recently in my choices, eating, actions or thoughts:

My new awareness today is:

For tomorrow, I want to remember:

My WHY. I commit and recommit to this SO THAT...

NOURISH DAILY PRACTICE LIST

DATE:

Morning Practice

My focus word for today is:

Today I want to NOURISH myself with (and by):

I am committed to my changes today because I want...

Evening Awareness and Gratitude

Things that might NOT have been nourishing recently in my choices, eating, actions or thoughts:

My new awareness today is:

For tomorrow, I want to remember:

My WHY. I commit and recommit to this SO THAT...

NOURISH DAILY PRACTICE LIST

DATE:

Morning Practice

My focus word for today is:

Today I want to NOURISH myself with (and by):

I am committed to my changes today because I want...

Evening Awareness and Gratitude

Things that might NOT have been nourishing recently in my choices, eating, actions or thoughts:

My new awareness today is:

For tomorrow, I want to remember:

My WHY. I commit and recommit to this SO THAT...

NOURISH DAILY PRACTICE LIST

DATE:

Morning Practice

My focus word for today is:

Today I want to NOURISH myself with (and by):

I am committed to my changes today because I want...

Evening Awareness and Gratitude

Things that might NOT have been nourishing recently in my choices, eating, actions or thoughts:

My new awareness today is:

For tomorrow, I want to remember:

My WHY. I commit and recommit to this SO THAT...

NOURISH DAILY PRACTICE LIST

DATE:

Morning Practice

My focus word for today is:

Today I want to NOURISH myself with (and by):

I am committed to my changes today because I want...

Evening Awareness and Gratitude

Things that might NOT have been nourishing recently in my choices, eating, actions or thoughts:

My new awareness today is:

For tomorrow, I want to remember:

My WHY. I commit and recommit to this SO THAT...

NOURISH DAILY PRACTICE LIST

DATE:

Morning Practice

My focus word for today is:

Today I want to NOURISH myself with (and by):

I am committed to my changes today because I want...

Evening Awareness and Gratitude

Things that might NOT have been nourishing recently in my choices, eating, actions or thoughts:

My new awareness today is:

For tomorrow, I want to remember:

My WHY. I commit and recommit to this SO THAT...

NOURISH DAILY PRACTICE LIST

DATE:

Morning Practice

My focus word for today is:

Today I want to NOURISH myself with (and by):

I am committed to my changes today because I want...

Evening Awareness and Gratitude

Things that might NOT have been nourishing recently in my choices, eating, actions or thoughts:

My new awareness today is:

For tomorrow, I want to remember:

My WHY. I commit and recommit to this SO THAT...

NOURISH DAILY PRACTICE LIST

DATE:

Morning Practice

My focus word for today is:

Today I want to NOURISH myself with (and by):

I am committed to my changes today because I want...

Evening Awareness and Gratitude

Things that might NOT have been nourishing recently in my choices, eating, actions or thoughts:

My new awareness today is:

For tomorrow, I want to remember:

My WHY. I commit and recommit to this SO THAT...

NOURISH DAILY PRACTICE LIST

DATE:

Morning Practice

My focus word for today is:

Today I want to NOURISH myself with (and by):

I am committed to my changes today because I want...

Evening Awareness and Gratitude

Things that might NOT have been nourishing recently in my choices, eating, actions or thoughts:

My new awareness today is:

For tomorrow, I want to remember:

My WHY. I commit and recommit to this SO THAT...

NOURISH DAILY PRACTICE LIST

DATE:

Morning Practice

My focus word for today is:

Today I want to NOURISH myself with (and by):

I am committed to my changes today because I want...

Evening Awareness and Gratitude

Things that might NOT have been nourishing recently in my choices, eating, actions or thoughts:

My new awareness today is:

For tomorrow, I want to remember:

My WHY. I commit and recommit to this SO THAT...

NOURISH DAILY PRACTICE LIST

DATE:

Morning Practice

My focus word for today is:

Today I want to NOURISH myself with (and by):

I am committed to my changes today because I want...

Evening Awareness and Gratitude

Things that might NOT have been nourishing recently in my choices, eating, actions or thoughts:

My new awareness today is:

For tomorrow, I want to remember:

My WHY. I commit and recommit to this SO THAT...

NOURISH DAILY PRACTICE LIST

DATE:

Morning Practice

My focus word for today is:

Today I want to NOURISH myself with (and by):

I am committed to my changes today because I want...

Evening Awareness and Gratitude

Things that might NOT have been nourishing recently in my choices, eating, actions or thoughts:

My new awareness today is:

For tomorrow, I want to remember:

My WHY. I commit and recommit to this SO THAT...

NOURISH DAILY PRACTICE LIST

DATE:

Morning Practice

My focus word for today is:

Today I want to NOURISH myself with (and by):

I am committed to my changes today because I want...

Evening Awareness and Gratitude

Things that might NOT have been nourishing recently in my choices, eating, actions or thoughts:

My new awareness today is:

For tomorrow, I want to remember:

My WHY. I commit and recommit to this SO THAT...

NOURISH DAILY PRACTICE LIST

DATE:

Morning Practice

My focus word for today is:

Today I want to NOURISH myself with (and by):

I am committed to my changes today because I want...

Evening Awareness and Gratitude

Things that might NOT have been nourishing recently in my choices, eating, actions or thoughts:

My new awareness today is:

For tomorrow, I want to remember:

My WHY. I commit and recommit to this SO THAT...

NOURISH DAILY PRACTICE LIST

DATE:

Morning Practice

My focus word for today is:

Today I want to NOURISH myself with (and by):

I am committed to my changes today because I want...

Evening Awareness and Gratitude

Things that might NOT have been nourishing recently in my choices, eating, actions or thoughts:

My new awareness today is:

For tomorrow, I want to remember:

My WHY. I commit and recommit to this SO THAT...

NOURISH DAILY PRACTICE LIST

DATE:

Morning Practice

My focus word for today is:

Today I want to NOURISH myself with (and by):

I am committed to my changes today because I want...

Evening Awareness and Gratitude

Things that might NOT have been nourishing recently in my choices, eating, actions or thoughts:

My new awareness today is:

For tomorrow, I want to remember:

My WHY. I commit and recommit to this SO THAT...

NOURISH DAILY PRACTICE LIST

DATE:

Morning Practice

My focus word for today is:

Today I want to NOURISH myself with (and by):

I am committed to my changes today because I want...

Evening Awareness and Gratitude

Things that might NOT have been nourishing recently in my choices, eating, actions or thoughts:

My new awareness today is:

For tomorrow, I want to remember:

My WHY. I commit and recommit to this SO THAT...

NOURISH DAILY PRACTICE LIST

DATE:

Morning Practice

My focus word for today is:

Today I want to NOURISH myself with (and by):

I am committed to my changes today because I want...

Evening Awareness and Gratitude

Things that might NOT have been nourishing recently in my choices, eating, actions or thoughts:

My new awareness today is:

For tomorrow, I want to remember:

My WHY. I commit and recommit to this SO THAT...

NOURISH DAILY PRACTICE LIST

DATE:

Morning Practice

My focus word for today is:

Today I want to NOURISH myself with (and by):

I am committed to my changes today because I want...

Evening Awareness and Gratitude

Things that might NOT have been nourishing recently in my choices, eating, actions or thoughts:

My new awareness today is:

For tomorrow, I want to remember:

My WHY. I commit and recommit to this SO THAT...

NOURISH DAILY PRACTICE LIST

DATE:

Morning Practice

My focus word for today is:

Today I want to NOURISH myself with (and by):

I am committed to my changes today because I want...

Evening Awareness and Gratitude

Things that might NOT have been nourishing recently in my choices, eating, actions or thoughts:

My new awareness today is:

For tomorrow, I want to remember:

My WHY. I commit and recommit to this SO THAT...

NOURISH DAILY PRACTICE LIST

DATE:

Morning Practice

My focus word for today is:

Today I want to NOURISH myself with (and by):

I am committed to my changes today because I want...

Evening Awareness and Gratitude

Things that might NOT have been nourishing recently in my choices, eating, actions or thoughts:

My new awareness today is:

For tomorrow, I want to remember:

My WHY. I commit and recommit to this SO THAT...

NOURISH DAILY PRACTICE LIST

DATE:

Morning Practice

My focus word for today is:

Today I want to NOURISH myself with (and by):

I am committed to my changes today because I want...

Evening Awareness and Gratitude

Things that might NOT have been nourishing recently in my choices, eating, actions or thoughts:

My new awareness today is:

For tomorrow, I want to remember:

My WHY. I commit and recommit to this SO THAT...

NOURISH DAILY PRACTICE LIST

DATE:

Morning Practice

My focus word for today is:

Today I want to NOURISH myself with (and by):

I am committed to my changes today because I want...

Evening Awareness and Gratitude

Things that might NOT have been nourishing recently in my choices, eating, actions or thoughts:

My new awareness today is:

For tomorrow, I want to remember:

My WHY. I commit and recommit to this SO THAT...

NOURISH DAILY PRACTICE LIST

DATE:

Morning Practice

My focus word for today is:

Today I want to NOURISH myself with (and by):

I am committed to my changes today because I want...

Evening Awareness and Gratitude

Things that might NOT have been nourishing recently in my choices, eating, actions or thoughts:

My new awareness today is:

For tomorrow, I want to remember:

My WHY. I commit and recommit to this SO THAT...

NOURISH DAILY PRACTICE LIST

DATE:

Morning Practice

My focus word for today is:

Today I want to NOURISH myself with (and by):

I am committed to my changes today because I want...

Evening Awareness and Gratitude

Things that might NOT have been nourishing recently in my choices, eating, actions or thoughts:

My new awareness today is:

For tomorrow, I want to remember:

My WHY. I commit and recommit to this SO THAT...

NOURISH DAILY PRACTICE LIST

DATE:

Morning Practice

My focus word for today is:

Today I want to NOURISH myself with (and by):

I am committed to my changes today because I want...

Evening Awareness and Gratitude

Things that might NOT have been nourishing recently in my choices, eating, actions or thoughts:

My new awareness today is:

For tomorrow, I want to remember:

My WHY. I commit and recommit to this SO THAT...

NOURISH DAILY PRACTICE LIST

DATE:

Morning Practice

My focus word for today is:

Today I want to NOURISH myself with (and by):

I am committed to my changes today because I want...

Evening Awareness and Gratitude

Things that might NOT have been nourishing recently in my choices, eating, actions or thoughts:

My new awareness today is:

For tomorrow, I want to remember:

My WHY. I commit and recommit to this SO THAT...

NOURISH DAILY PRACTICE LIST

DATE:

Morning Practice

My focus word for today is:

Today I want to NOURISH myself with (and by):

I am committed to my changes today because I want...

Evening Awareness and Gratitude

Things that might NOT have been nourishing recently in my choices, eating, actions or thoughts:

My new awareness today is:

For tomorrow, I want to remember:

My WHY. I commit and recommit to this SO THAT...

NOURISH DAILY PRACTICE LIST

DATE:

Morning Practice

My focus word for today is:

Today I want to NOURISH myself with (and by):

I am committed to my changes today because I want...

Evening Awareness and Gratitude

Things that might NOT have been nourishing recently in my choices, eating, actions or thoughts:

My new awareness today is:

For tomorrow, I want to remember:

My WHY. I commit and recommit to this SO THAT...

NOURISH DAILY PRACTICE LIST

DATE:

Morning Practice

My focus word for today is:

Today I want to NOURISH myself with (and by):

I am committed to my changes today because I want...

Evening Awareness and Gratitude

Things that might NOT have been nourishing recently in my choices, eating, actions or thoughts:

My new awareness today is:

For tomorrow, I want to remember:

My WHY. I commit and recommit to this SO THAT...

NOURISH DAILY PRACTICE LIST

DATE:

Morning Practice

My focus word for today is:

Today I want to NOURISH myself with (and by):

I am committed to my changes today because I want...

Evening Awareness and Gratitude

Things that might NOT have been nourishing recently in my choices, eating, actions or thoughts:

My new awareness today is:

For tomorrow, I want to remember:

My WHY. I commit and recommit to this SO THAT...

NOURISH DAILY PRACTICE LIST

DATE:

Morning Practice

My focus word for today is:

Today I want to NOURISH myself with (and by):

I am committed to my changes today because I want...

Evening Awareness and Gratitude

Things that might NOT have been nourishing recently in my choices, eating, actions or thoughts:

My new awareness today is:

For tomorrow, I want to remember:

My WHY. I commit and recommit to this SO THAT...

NOURISH DAILY PRACTICE LIST

DATE:

Morning Practice

My focus word for today is:

Today I want to NOURISH myself with (and by):

I am committed to my changes today because I want...

Evening Awareness and Gratitude

Things that might NOT have been nourishing recently in my choices, eating, actions or thoughts:

My new awareness today is:

For tomorrow, I want to remember:

My WHY. I commit and recommit to this SO THAT...

NOURISH DAILY PRACTICE LIST

DATE:

Morning Practice

My focus word for today is:

Today I want to NOURISH myself with (and by):

I am committed to my changes today because I want...

Evening Awareness and Gratitude

Things that might NOT have been nourishing recently in my choices, eating, actions or thoughts:

My new awareness today is:

For tomorrow, I want to remember:

My WHY. I commit and recommit to this SO THAT...

NOURISH DAILY PRACTICE LIST

DATE:

Morning Practice

My focus word for today is:

Today I want to NOURISH myself with (and by):

I am committed to my changes today because I want...

Evening Awareness and Gratitude

Things that might NOT have been nourishing recently in my choices, eating, actions or thoughts:

My new awareness today is:

For tomorrow, I want to remember:

My WHY. I commit and recommit to this SO THAT...

NOURISH DAILY PRACTICE LIST

DATE:

Morning Practice

My focus word for today is:

Today I want to NOURISH myself with (and by):

I am committed to my changes today because I want...

Evening Awareness and Gratitude

Things that might NOT have been nourishing recently in my choices, eating, actions or thoughts:

My new awareness today is:

For tomorrow, I want to remember:

My WHY. I commit and recommit to this SO THAT...

NOURISH DAILY PRACTICE LIST

DATE:

Morning Practice

My focus word for today is:

Today I want to NOURISH myself with (and by):

I am committed to my changes today because I want...

Evening Awareness and Gratitude

Things that might NOT have been nourishing recently in my choices, eating, actions or thoughts:

My new awareness today is:

For tomorrow, I want to remember:

My WHY. I commit and recommit to this SO THAT...

NOURISH DAILY PRACTICE LIST

DATE:

Morning Practice

My focus word for today is:

Today I want to NOURISH myself with (and by):

I am committed to my changes today because I want...

Evening Awareness and Gratitude

Things that might NOT have been nourishing recently in my choices, eating, actions or thoughts:

My new awareness today is:

For tomorrow, I want to remember:

My WHY. I commit and recommit to this SO THAT...

NOURISH DAILY PRACTICE LIST

DATE:

Morning Practice

My focus word for today is:

Today I want to NOURISH myself with (and by):

I am committed to my changes today because I want...

Evening Awareness and Gratitude

Things that might NOT have been nourishing recently in my choices, eating, actions or thoughts:

My new awareness today is:

For tomorrow, I want to remember:

My WHY. I commit and recommit to this SO THAT...

NOURISH DAILY PRACTICE LIST

DATE:

Morning Practice

My focus word for today is:

Today I want to NOURISH myself with (and by):

I am committed to my changes today because I want...

Evening Awareness and Gratitude

Things that might NOT have been nourishing recently in my choices, eating, actions or thoughts:

My new awareness today is:

For tomorrow, I want to remember:

My WHY. I commit and recommit to this SO THAT...

NOURISH DAILY PRACTICE LIST

DATE:

Morning Practice

My focus word for today is:

Today I want to NOURISH myself with (and by):

I am committed to my changes today because I want...

Evening Awareness and Gratitude

Things that might NOT have been nourishing recently in my choices, eating, actions or thoughts:

My new awareness today is:

For tomorrow, I want to remember:

My WHY. I commit and recommit to this SO THAT...

NOURISH DAILY PRACTICE LIST

DATE:

Morning Practice

My focus word for today is:

Today I want to NOURISH myself with (and by):

I am committed to my changes today because I want...

Evening Awareness and Gratitude

Things that might NOT have been nourishing recently in my choices, eating, actions or thoughts:

My new awareness today is:

For tomorrow, I want to remember:

My WHY. I commit and recommit to this SO THAT...

NOURISH DAILY PRACTICE LIST

DATE:

Morning Practice

My focus word for today is:

Today I want to NOURISH myself with (and by):

I am committed to my changes today because I want...

Evening Awareness and Gratitude

Things that might NOT have been nourishing recently in my choices, eating, actions or thoughts:

My new awareness today is:

For tomorrow, I want to remember:

My WHY. I commit and recommit to this SO THAT...

NOURISH DAILY PRACTICE LIST

DATE:

Morning Practice

My focus word for today is:

Today I want to NOURISH myself with (and by):

I am committed to my changes today because I want...

Evening Awareness and Gratitude

Things that might NOT have been nourishing recently in my choices, eating, actions or thoughts:

My new awareness today is:

For tomorrow, I want to remember:

My WHY. I commit and recommit to this SO THAT...

NOURISH DAILY PRACTICE LIST

DATE:

Morning Practice

My focus word for today is:

Today I want to NOURISH myself with (and by):

I am committed to my changes today because I want...

Evening Awareness and Gratitude

Things that might NOT have been nourishing recently in my choices, eating, actions or thoughts:

My new awareness today is:

For tomorrow, I want to remember:

My WHY. I commit and recommit to this SO THAT...

NOURISH DAILY PRACTICE LIST

DATE:

Morning Practice

My focus word for today is:

Today I want to NOURISH myself with (and by):

I am committed to my changes today because I want...

Evening Awareness and Gratitude

Things that might NOT have been nourishing recently in my choices, eating, actions or thoughts:

My new awareness today is:

For tomorrow, I want to remember:

My WHY. I commit and recommit to this SO THAT...

NOURISH DAILY PRACTICE LIST

DATE:

Morning Practice

My focus word for today is:

Today I want to NOURISH myself with (and by):

I am committed to my changes today because I want...

Evening Awareness and Gratitude

Things that might NOT have been nourishing recently in my choices, eating, actions or thoughts:

My new awareness today is:

For tomorrow, I want to remember:

My WHY. I commit and recommit to this SO THAT...

NOURISH DAILY PRACTICE LIST

DATE:

Morning Practice

My focus word for today is:

Today I want to NOURISH myself with (and by):

I am committed to my changes today because I want...

Evening Awareness and Gratitude

Things that might NOT have been nourishing recently in my choices, eating, actions or thoughts:

My new awareness today is:

For tomorrow, I want to remember:

My WHY. I commit and recommit to this SO THAT...

NOURISH DAILY PRACTICE LIST

DATE:

Morning Practice

My focus word for today is:

Today I want to NOURISH myself with (and by):

I am committed to my changes today because I want...

Evening Awareness and Gratitude

Things that might NOT have been nourishing recently in my choices, eating, actions or thoughts:

My new awareness today is:

For tomorrow, I want to remember:

My WHY. I commit and recommit to this SO THAT...

NOURISH DAILY PRACTICE LIST

DATE:

Morning Practice

My focus word for today is:

Today I want to NOURISH myself with (and by):

I am committed to my changes today because I want...

Evening Awareness and Gratitude

Things that might NOT have been nourishing recently in my choices, eating, actions or thoughts:

My new awareness today is:

For tomorrow, I want to remember:

My WHY. I commit and recommit to this SO THAT...

NOURISH DAILY PRACTICE LIST

DATE:

Morning Practice

My focus word for today is:

Today I want to NOURISH myself with (and by):

I am committed to my changes today because I want...

Evening Awareness and Gratitude

Things that might NOT have been nourishing recently in my choices, eating, actions or thoughts:

My new awareness today is:

For tomorrow, I want to remember:

My WHY. I commit and recommit to this SO THAT...

NOURISH DAILY PRACTICE LIST

DATE:

Morning Practice

My focus word for today is:

Today I want to NOURISH myself with (and by):

I am committed to my changes today because I want...

Evening Awareness and Gratitude

Things that might NOT have been nourishing recently in my choices, eating, actions or thoughts:

My new awareness today is:

For tomorrow, I want to remember:

My WHY. I commit and recommit to this SO THAT...

NOURISH DAILY PRACTICE LIST

DATE:

Morning Practice

My focus word for today is:

Today I want to NOURISH myself with (and by):

I am committed to my changes today because I want...

Evening Awareness and Gratitude

Things that might NOT have been nourishing recently in my choices, eating, actions or thoughts:

My new awareness today is:

For tomorrow, I want to remember:

My WHY. I commit and recommit to this SO THAT...

NOURISH DAILY PRACTICE LIST

DATE:

Morning Practice

My focus word for today is:

Today I want to NOURISH myself with (and by):

I am committed to my changes today because I want...

Evening Awareness and Gratitude

Things that might NOT have been nourishing recently in my choices, eating, actions or thoughts:

My new awareness today is:

For tomorrow, I want to remember:

My WHY. I commit and recommit to this SO THAT...

NOURISH DAILY PRACTICE LIST

DATE:

Morning Practice

My focus word for today is:

Today I want to NOURISH myself with (and by):

I am committed to my changes today because I want...

Evening Awareness and Gratitude

Things that might NOT have been nourishing recently in my choices, eating, actions or thoughts:

My new awareness today is:

For tomorrow, I want to remember:

My WHY. I commit and recommit to this SO THAT...

NOURISH NOTES

NOURISH NOTES

NOURISH NOTES

NOURISH NOTES

NOURISH NOTES

NOURISH NOTES

ABOUT
DIANE CUNNINGHAM ELLIS

Diane Cunningham Ellis, M.Ed. is a "renaissance woman" who lives with her heart on her sleeve and a permanent smile on her face.

She creates. She is a cheerleader to all those she meets. She is a creativity coach, a pied piper of people, a woman of vulnerability, and a passionate heart artist. She loves to provide women with opportunities to go on brave adventures near and far. She coaches women (and a few brave men) on business, life, recovery, authentic living, and so much more.

She coaches. Diane is a "business therapist," plane crash survivor, author, consultant, speaker, marathon runner, and fun friend. She eats in various nourishing ways and is always exploring in her food plan. She has weighed 203 pounds at her highest weight and 122 pounds at her lowest and now is currently embracing life at a healthy weight for her body, frame, and lifestyle.

She leads. She has a Master's Degree in Education (Guidance and Counseling) from Whitworth College in Spokane, Washington, as well as a Bachelor's Degree in Interpersonal Communications. She is a woman living in recovery and is now a Life Recovery Coach, along with all of her other coaching programs.

She is the Founder of the National Association of Christian Women Entrepreneurs®, a global association where women meet to connect, create, and collaborate. NACWE offers training, conferences, networking, and business strategies. NACWE was launched in May 2010 and has been building and expanding since that time with members throughout the United States and Canada. She served as President for seven years (2010-2017).

She writes. Diane is the author of seven books and counting, four which are Amazon Bestsellers, including *The Inspired Business Toolkit* and the *Rock Bottom is a Beautiful Place* book series.

She laughs. She currently lives in the Dallas, Texas area. Her house looks like a book store, art gallery, and office supply store merged. She is messy and has learned to embrace her glorious mess.

She loves. Diane is a heart girl and loves people relentlessly. She gives, she serves, she loves bravely. She is happily married to Jim, her very own Private Investigator.

940-247-0090
DIANE@DIANECUNNINGHAM.COM
DIANECUNNINGHAM.COM
FACEBOOK.COM/DIANECUNNINGHAM
FACEBOOK.COM/DIANECUNNINGHAMFRIENDS
YOUTUBE.COM/USER/LIFECOACHDIANE

The **BRAVE CREATIONS**™ Nourishment Series

Coming Soon!

The Transformation Tracker
Nourish: How to Live a Satisfied Life
The Art of Enough: Daily Meditations on Nourishment
The Year of Nourishing
The Nourishment Project
ReStart: The Art of Starting Over

Other Books by Diane Cunningham Ellis

Inspired Business Toolkit
Rock Bottom is A Beautiful Place Series
Inspired Women Succeed
The Art of Brave Living
Dear Female Entrepreneur, My Friend

Information about all of these books and workbooks can be found at
www.DianeCunningham.com, along with links to their Amazon listings.

ONE BRAVE AT A TIME.
CHOOSE TO NOURISH.

Made in the USA
Monee, IL
27 February 2020